If the Candles Co

The Story Of Chanukah

Written by **Dassie Prus**

Illustrated by **Michael Graham**

Jewish Big Books Publishing

If the Candles Could Speak
Author: Dassie Prus
Illustrator: Michael Graham

Jewish Big Books Publishing
www.JewishBigBooks.com

ISBN-13: 978-1-7325237-0-8

If the Candles Could Speak is
also available in a Big Book edition.
Other books in this series:
The Purim Big Book - The Story of Esther

Printed in China

As we sit and watch the Chanukah flames burn,
the candles start speaking, each one takes a turn.
The story of Chanukah, we begin to hear,
and why there's a holiday at this time of year.

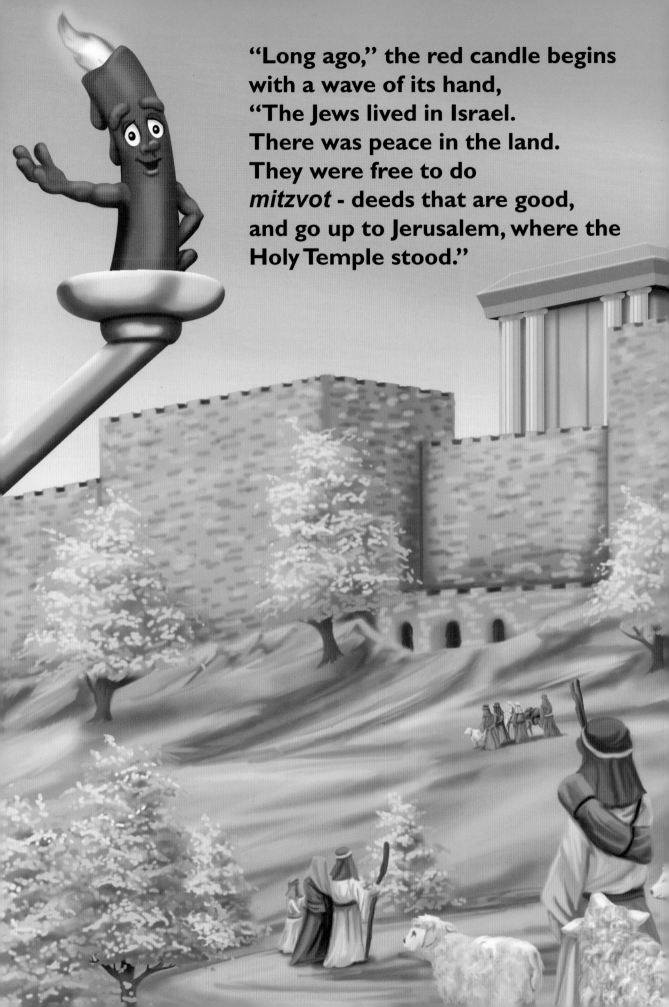

"Long ago," the red candle begins
with a wave of its hand,
"The Jews lived in Israel.
There was peace in the land.
They were free to do
mitzvot - deeds that are good,
and go up to Jerusalem, where the
Holy Temple stood."

The purple candle tells of
a mighty Greek king,
who came with new rules
and changed everything.

King Antiochus

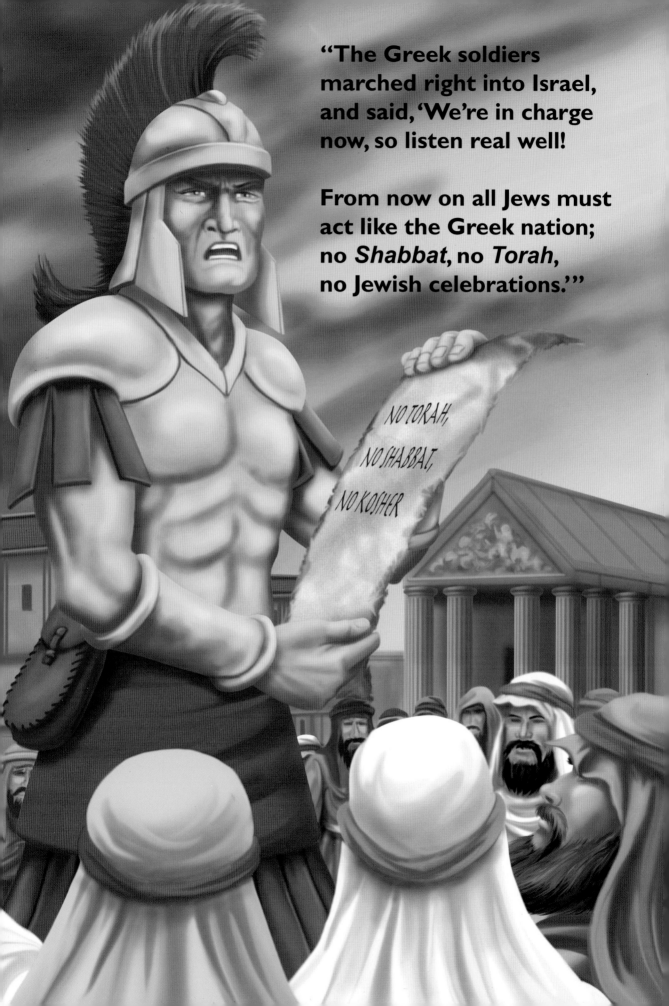

"'Your schools and your synagogues
will all be closed down.
And we'll put an idol in the center of town!

The Temple is ours;
no Jews can come near.'
They stopped the holy service
the Jews held so dear."

The white candle continues,
its light shining bright,
"Then brave men cried out,
'We'll stand up for what's right!'

They made a small army
called the Maccabees,
and moved to the hills
with their families.

They refused to bow down
to the idols, you see.
They knew there's just one
G-d and fought to be free.
Their leader was Yehuda,
Judah the Maccabee."

The next candle speaks,
its color is blue,
"The Maccabees wondered,
'Now what will we do?
The Greeks are so many
and we are so few!

Their army is strong;
there are none to compare.
Can we go out to battle?
Can we fight? Do we dare?'"

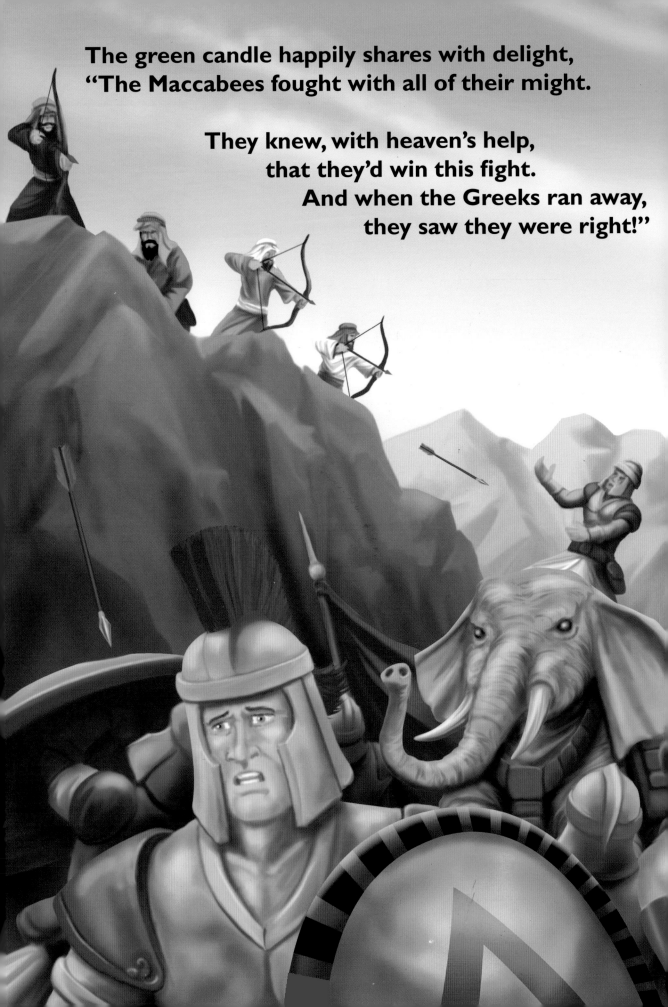

The green candle happily shares with delight,
"The Maccabees fought with all of their might.

They knew, with heaven's help,
that they'd win this fight.
And when the Greeks ran away,
they saw they were right!"

The glowing yellow candle
can no longer sit,
excited to tell how the
Jews would not quit.

"The Maccabees came into
the Holy Temple at last.
They cleaned up the mess;
they did it so fast.

They set up the Menorah,
stood it tall on the ground,
but oil to light it was nowhere to be found.
What oil was needed -- do you have a clue?
Only olive oil in a sealed jug would do."

The joyful orange candle lets out a cheer,
"The miracle of Chanukah, I'd like to share!
They searched 'til they found some oil -- just a bit.
The only jug with a seal on it!

It was enough oil to light for only one day.
But it would take eight days to bring more from far away.
This was a *mitzvah* they would not delay,
so they lit the Menorah right then, right away."

1 2 3 4

"Amazed, they all watched as
the bright holy lights,
kept burning and burning
for eight days and nights."

The proud pink candle goes on to relate,
"These miracles make this holiday great.

Jews around the world each year celebrate,
by lighting their candles on
nights one through eight."

As we watch the candles slowly flicker good-bye,
we thank them for the story and then -- oh my!
The tall candle calls out, "Don't pass me by!
I am the *shamash* with a wish from up high.

You should all be brave Maccabees,
stand up for what's right.
And throughout the whole year
spread the Chanukah light.

You can do acts of goodness and kindness,
little things, one by one,
and make the world better,
a better place for everyone."

Happy Chanukah!

How Do We Celebrate
Chanukah?

We love lighting our Menorah, that's for sure,
with colored candles or olive oil so pure.
When the sun goes down and the day is done,
it's time to begin the Chanukah fun.

Set up the candles in a nice straight row.
The tallest spot is where the *shamash* will go.
Light up the *shamash*, hold it near,
and say your blessings, loud and clear.

Light the candles, start with the new one,
and sing happy Chanukah songs with everyone!
For eight nights, we light it, with the *shamash* standing tall,
adding each night 'til there are eight lights in all.

HAY

Twirl your dreidel; see the top spin,
with the Hebrew letters
nun, gimmel, hey, shin.

And remember the brave
children so long ago,
who learned *Torah* in hiding
when the Greeks told them, "No!"

SHIN

Latkes, potato pancakes, are a Chanukah treat.
They're fried in oil, so tasty to eat!

Suganiot are doughnuts fried in oil.
Wow, watch how they boil!

They're sprinkled with sugar
and filled with sweet jelly.
Don't eat too many or they may hurt your belly!

Chanukah presents! You love them, I bet,
or maybe it's money that you will get.
Chocolate *gelt* coins taste really yummy.
Gelt is the Yiddish word for money.

The Dreidel Game

Dreidel is a game played during Chanukah. The dreidel is a top with four sides, each with a different Hebrew letter printed on it.

How to play dreidel:

- Hand out an equal amount of chocolate coins, pennies, or similar small items to each player, and place a sizable pile of the same items in the center.

- The first player spins the dreidel. Each letter has another rule.

Nun: You get nothing.

Gimmel: You win the whole pot in the center of the table.

Hay: You win half the pot.

Shin: You must put one coin into the pot.

- Continue the game with players taking turns to spin the dreidel.

- Have each player place one coin or item into the pot every time it empties completely.

- Play until one player has earned all the coins at the table.

The four letters on the dreidel are **nun, gimmel, hay, shin**. They stand for the Hebrew words, **nes gadol haya sham**, "A great miracle happened there."

In Israel the dreidel has the letter **pey** instead of a shin. They stand for the Hebrew words, **nes gadol haya po**, "A great miracle happened here."

Chanukah Glossary:
Explanation of Terms and Concepts

Chanukah: Hanukkah. This eight day holiday celebrates two miracles. The first is the great victory of the small Maccabbee army over the mighty Greeks. The second is the miracle of the oil. When the Maccabees freed the Temple from the hands of the Greeks, they found that only a small jug of olive oil was left sealed and pure for lighting the Menorah. The problem was, it was only enough to light the Menorah for one day and it would take eight days to produce new pure oil. Miraculously, the little jug of oil burned for eight days and eight nights.

Chocolate Gelt: Chocolate coins wrapped in gold or silver foil.

Dreidel: The Yiddish word for a four-sided top; traditionally played as a Chanukah game.

Gelt: Money in Yiddish. There is a custom to give children Chanukah gelt on Chanukah add enjoyment to their holiday. This is an opportunity for children to learn how to give charity from their own money.

Holy Temple: The first and second Temples stood in Jerusalem. They were the center of Jewish life, a place where the presence of G-d could be felt. The story of Chanukah happened during the time of the second Temple.

Latkes: Potato pancakes fried in oil and eaten on Chanukah to remember the miracle of the oil.

Maccabee: The brave Jews who fought against the powerful Greek army. The word Maccabee is an acronym for the Hebrew words: *Mi Kamocha Ba'eilim Hashem*, "Who is like You, O G-d."

Menorah: A candelabra with eight branches and a ninth taller one that is lit during Chanukah. The Menorah in the Holy Temple had seven even branches and was made of pure gold. It was lit every day with pure olive oil.

Mitzvah: One of the 613 commandments in the Torah; a good deed.

Mitzvot: Plural for mitzvah.

Nun, Gimmel, Hay, Shin: Hebrew letters that are found on the dreidel. They stand for ***Nes Gadol Hayah Sham***, "A great miracle happened there." In Israel the dreidel has the letter pey instead of a shin. They stands for, ***Nes Gadol Haya Po***, "A great miracle happened here."

Shabbat: The Jewish Sabbath. A day of rest and family togetherness celebrated every week from sunset on Friday to nightfall on Saturday. Some Shabbat observances include: lighting the candles before sunset, making a blessing on wine and challah bread, eating and singing, praying and studying, taking a break from work and sharing time with family.

Shamash: The "helper" candle that is used to light the other eight lights of the menorah. This candle usually sits higher up so it stands out.

Sufganiot: Jelly donuts fried in oil. They are traditionally eaten in Israel to remember the miracle of the oil.

Torah: The five books of Moses. It is Judaism's most holy book. The Torah is written on a scroll of cow's hide parchment and used in synagogue services. The Torah in a printed book is called a Chumash.

Yiddish: A language spoken by many Jews.